THIS BOOK BELONGS TO

_____

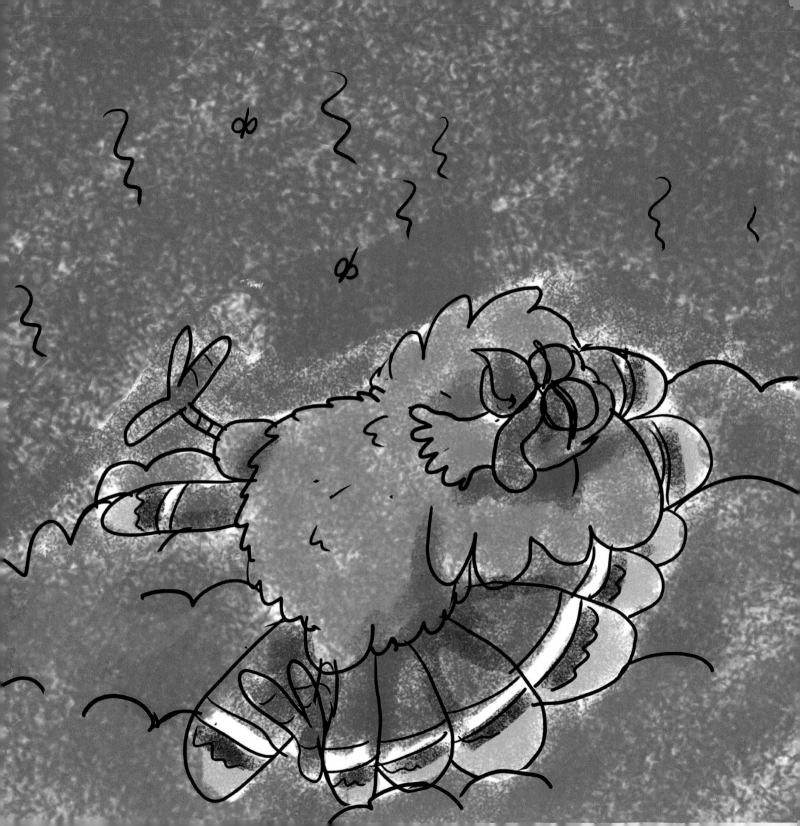

Taylor the Tooting Turkey

by Humor Heals Us

The Silent Killer
The deadly but silent killer - This one comes out so fast and quiet with no sound whatsoever, yet stinks more than all other toots.
It's the kind of toot where if done in public, you're so glad it's silent. If you accidentally get a whiff of your own fatal toot, you feel embarrassed, even though no one will ever really know it was you.

The Classic Loud Scream

This happens when your stomach makes the weirdest, loudest sound. You can feel the gas moving in your stomach, trying to find its way out, while your stomach has that uneasy feeling.

Then, the glorious moment when you can toot it out, loud and proud, you get a feeling of satisfaction and accomplishment.

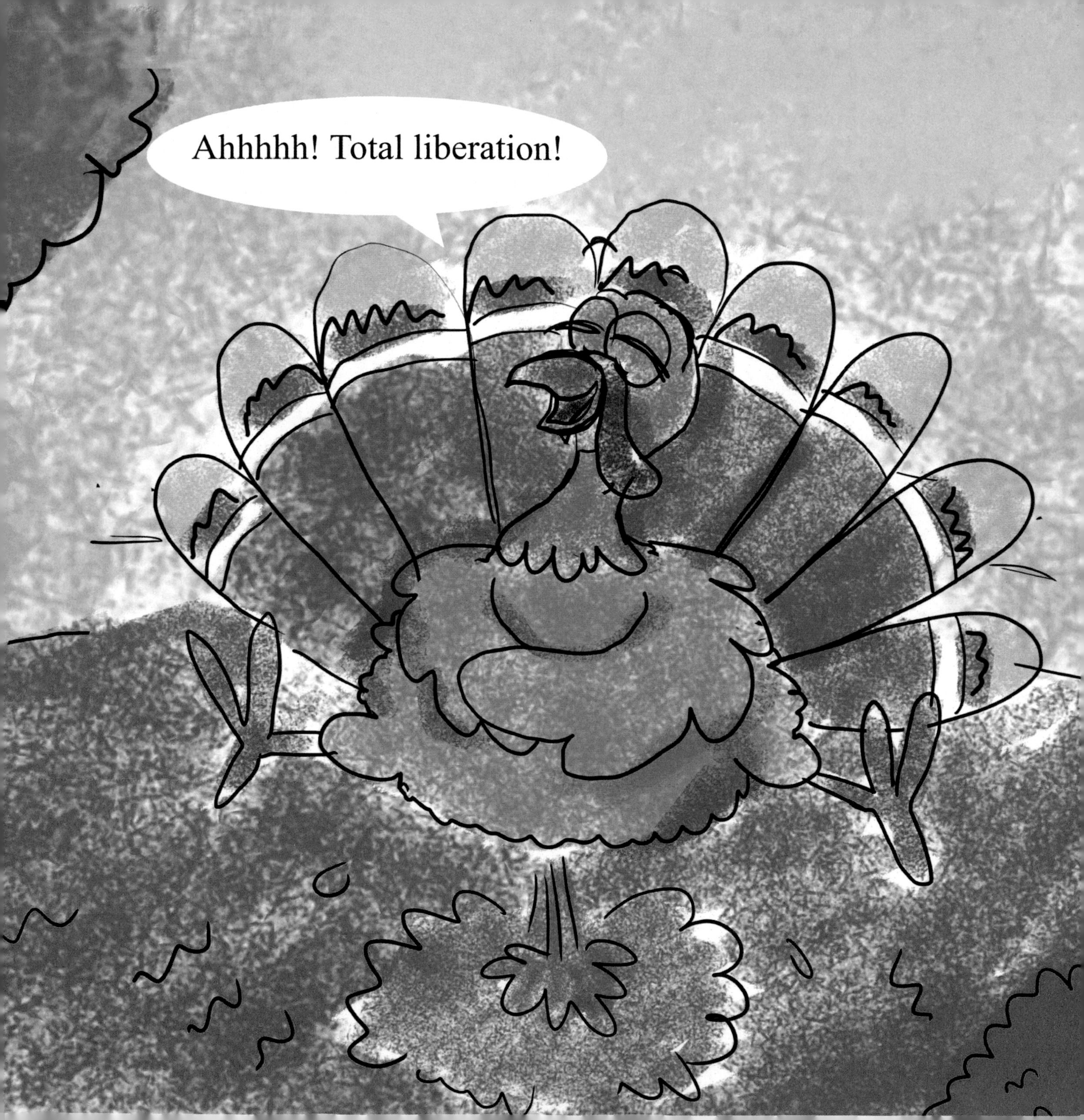
Ahhhhh! Total liberation!

The False Alarm
This is not a satisfying toot. The 'false alarm' toot is the kind when you thought you needed to take a poop, so you run for the bathroom, only to realize that you didn't need to poop – you just needed to toot. It was just a toot in disguise, darn it!

The Laughing Toot
This is probably THE MOST embarrassing toot of all toots. You are talking with a friend, laughing when a toot escapes your butt, and it's not a quiet one either.

The Bathtub Toot

This is the only toot you can see. You don't actually see the toot, but what you see is the bubbles.

The Bathtub Toot can be either single or multiple bubbles, depending on how big the toot is.

The Crowd Toot
The Crowd Toot got its name by its very potent odor, strong enough to make quite a few people look around. The trick here is not to identify the toot but the tooter.

This is almost impossible unless the tooter panics, and starts a fit of coughing or starts staring at the ceiling or the sky as though something up there fascinates him. In which case he is the one. Super common.

Do you smell that?

Who cut the cheese?

So you see? You may have experienced one or more of these kinds of toots which makes you a Tooting Turkey, too…

Frank the Farting Flamingo.

To vote on new title names and freebies,
visit us at humorhealsus.com
for more information.

Follow us on

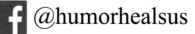 @humorhealsus

 @humorhealsus

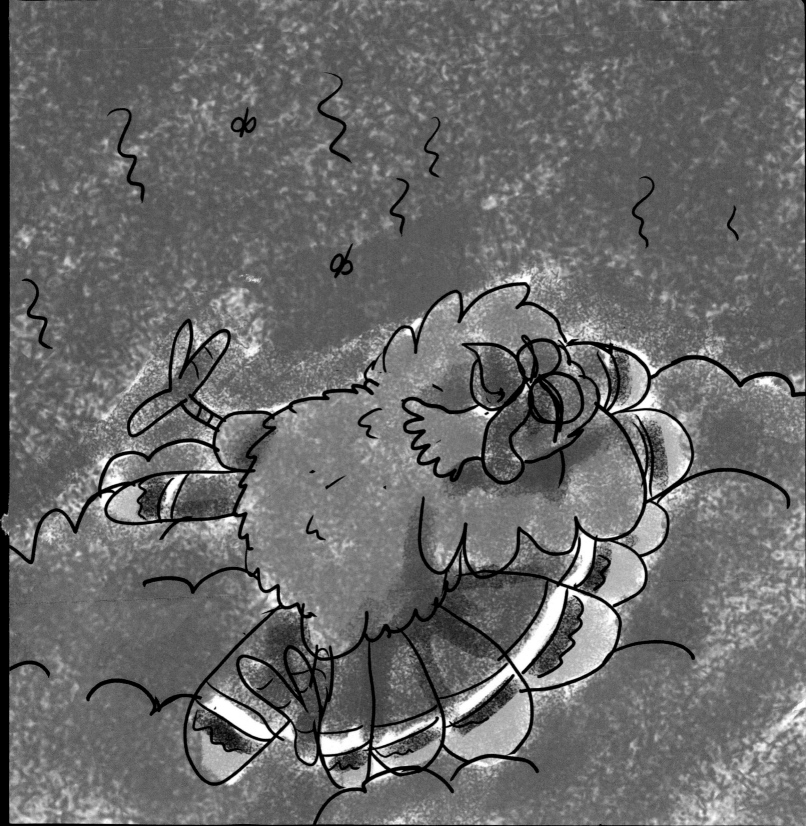

Made in the USA
Columbia, SC
04 December 2021